ESCAPE
FROM THYFERRA

#2
Escape from Thyferra

RYDER WINDHAM

SCHOLASTIC INC.

New York Toronto London Auckland Sydney

No part of this publication may be reproduced in whole or in part, or stored in a retrieval sys-tem, or transmitted in any form or by any means, electronic, mechanical, photocopying, recording, or otherwise, without written permission of the publisher. For information regard-ing permission, write to Scholastic Inc., 555 Broadway, New York, NY 10012.

ISBN 0-590-12794-2

12 11 10 9 8 7 6 5 4 3 2 1   7 8 9/9 0 1 2/0

Printed in the U.S.A.

First Scholastic printing, October 1997

ESCAPE
FROM THYFERRA

PRELIMINARY MISSION

CHAPTER ONE

Where was the Death Star? Admiral Termo knew something was wrong when it did not arrive at the Delrakkin system at the appointed time. There was no reason for the delay, unless the battle station had been . . . *destroyed.*

Admiral Termo left the bridge of the Imperial Star Destroyer *Liquidator* and went to his private quarters. Once there, he punched in the combination for a small safe concealed in his desk. A panel slid open, revealing three holotapes marked EMERGENCY ONLY.

The holotapes had been given to Termo by Grand Moff Tarkin. The Admiral sat down in his chair and inserted the first one into a holoprojector. Termo pressed a button, then waited.

The hologram glowed green as it flickered into focus. Termo instantly recognized the lean, hawklike features of Grand Moff Tarkin.

"Admiral Termo," spoke the ghostly hologram. "If you are viewing this holotape, it is because I was not able to transmit a message from the Death Star to the Delrakkin system at the designated hour. Of even greater concern, I ordered you to wait for the Death Star at Delrakkin, and we have not yet arrived.

"Because you do not know the full details of your mission," continued Tarkin's flickering image, "I am sure you must be confused. I am making this message as a mere precaution. I do this to stress the importance of your mission."

Admiral Termo leaned closer to the hologram. He

studied Grand Moff Tarkin's expression, trying to see if the old face seemed worried.

"Wait until 0300 hours, Admiral," instructed Tarkin's green hologram, "then send a coded transmission to destination B90-478R. I cannot divulge the name of your contact, but assure you that he is of extremely high rank."

Probably another Grand Moff, thought Termo.

"If the Death Star arrives before 0300 hours," continued the Tarkin hologram, "disregard this communication, and destroy the second and third holotapes. That is all for now, Admiral."

For a moment, the hologram glowed even more brightly, then seemed to turn away as the green light faded to empty air.

Termo pressed a button for the ship's comm. "Admiral Termo to Communications Officer Tix. Any sign of the Death Star?"

"No, Admiral," replied Tix from the bridge.

"Keep me posted," ordered Termo. He switched off the comm.

Termo turned and looked out his small window to see scores of distant stars. "What could possibly have happened at Yavin?" Termo wondered aloud.

Deep within the Rebel base on Yavin Four, General Dodonna walked down a long corridor. The Rebels were conserving power, so only one portable light hung in the dim walkway. But as the General reached the end of the hall, he saw a familiar droid's eyes glowing in the darkness.

"Thank you for coming so quickly, General," said the golden droid.

"What's going on, Threepio?" Dodonna asked. He appeared tired. See-Threepio had used a comm unit to contact the General, but the droid did know that Dodonna had been sleeping at the time.

"I hope you'll forgive me, General," Threepio pleaded, "but I was instructed not to say anything more over the comm. Won't you please come inside? The others are waiting."

In the room, Dodonna found Princess Leia, Luke Skywalker, and Han Solo seated at a round table. Chewbacca the Wookiee stood against the wall.

"General Dodonna," Princess Leia began immediately, "we're sorry to disturb you at this late hour, but we have come across some information that may be of great importance to the Rebel Alliance."

The sleepiness vanished from General Dodonna's eyes. He was suddenly alert. Nodding his head toward Leia, he said, "Go on."

"We know that the Death Star was carrying a large supply of bacta," Leia reported. "Although the bacta was destroyed, we were curious about this information. We wondered why the Empire would want so much bacta since it is used to heal people."

"That is puzzling," Dodonna agreed. "The Empire would sooner destroy an entire civilization than heal a single person."

"We thought the same thing, General," Luke offered. "But then we learned from the captured Imperial captain that the Death Star's bacta was *contaminated*!"

"All over the galaxy," Leia continued, "people trust that bacta can heal almost any wound. The Death Star was carrying enough bacta for a small city. I believe that the Empire was planning to use their contaminated bacta as a biological weapon!"

"What?!" said Dodonna. "You mean they planned to use bacta to poison a city? But that makes even *less* sense. The Death Star was capable of destroying whole worlds. Why would the Empire want to use contaminated bacta as a weapon?"

"Maybe there is a world that the Empire doesn't want to destroy," Solo suggested. "They need the planet, but not the people on it."

"Exactly," Leia stated. "If this is what the Empire intended, the plan may not have ended with the destruction of the Death Star. There may be more contaminated bacta out there — *anywhere.* If there is a city or world that's in danger, we have to try to help."

General Dodonna cast his eyes down at the table before he spoke. "Can we get any more information out of the captured Imperial captain?"

Chewbacca uttered a low, menacing growl.

"Captain Skeezer refuses to tell us anything more," Solo reported. "But Chewie has just offered to *make* Skeezer talk."

"Please, Solo, let's not resort to *that*," said a surprised Dodonna. "The Empire endorses extreme methods of questioning, but I do not. There are other ways to gain information. What about his crashed ship? Were there any records of where the ship came from or why it entered the Yavin system?"

"There wasn't any record of origin on the Carrack cruiser's computers," Luke answered. "Captain Skeezer may have been on a secret mission. The good news is that the Carrack cruiser is in pretty good shape despite the crash. We've got three teams of technicians working on it. It should be repaired in a couple of days."

"That *is* good news," Dodonna agreed. "We can add that ship to the Rebel fleet. But about the bacta. How do you think we should proceed, Leia?"

"There is only one planet in the galaxy that produces bacta," Leia stated. "Thyferra, in the Polith system. We have a contact on Thyferra, a woman named Voralla Morbo. She's helped the Rebellion when we needed to transport bacta. Perhaps she knows something about the Death Star cargo."

"Isn't Thyferra controlled by the Empire?" asked Luke.

"Not exactly," Leia replied. "Thyferra has remained neutral and sells bacta to both the Empire and the Alliance. However, the Empire controls much of the bacta production and distribution."

General Dodonna shook his head. "For all we know, the Death Star's contaminated bacta may have been made somewhere else."

"But General," pleaded Leia, "it's our only lead! Thyferra may prove to be a dead end, but we have to try!" Leia kept her voice firm when she added, "I will *not* lose *another* planet to the Empire!"

Silence filled the room. Everyone knew that the Princess referred to her home world, the planet Alderaan. Grand Moff Tarkin himself had ordered its destruction.

"Very well," Dodonna said. "How soon will you leave?"

"The *Millennium Falcon* is powered up and ready," Solo answered. "We can be out of here in five minutes."

"Oh, dear!" cried Threepio. "We're leaving *that* soon? I must get Artoo! He's still trying to fix that droid from the ancient fortress!"

Dodonna looked gravely at Leia. "I don't have to tell you to be careful," he said. He turned to the others and added, "But I will say . . . may the Force be with you."

CHAPTER TWO

Communications Officer Tix watched nervously as Admiral Termo paced on the bridge of the Imperial Star Destroyer. Finally, Termo turned to Tix and asked, "How long has it been since Captain Skeezer left this ship?"

"Twelve hours, sir," Tix responded.

Termo gazed out the viewport at the planet Delrakkin. Another storm was visible on the surface of the lush, green planet.

"Twelve hours," Termo echoed, "that should have been enough time for Captain Skeezer to reach the Yavin system, locate the Death Star, and report back to me."

Officer Tix remained silent. In the hours since Captain Skeezer had left the Star Destroyer, Tix had begun to wonder what could have happened to the Death Star. Perhaps the massive battle station had been struck by a gigantic meteor or had accidentally traveled into the area of a supernova (the explosion of a very large star). It was impossible to imagine that anything less could have destroyed the massive weapon. It was impossible to know what would happen to the Empire if the Death Star was . . . gone.

The *Millennium Falcon*'s engines roared as it flew swiftly away from Yavin Four. In the cockpit, Luke and Leia sat behind Solo and Chewbacca. An empty Y-wing starfighter was secured to the lower hull of the *Falcon*. The Y-wing could only seat two passengers, but General Dodonna had suggested the Rebels might need the extra vessel on Thyferra. Even Solo agreed that it was a good idea to have a backup ship.

The droids were in the central hold area of the *Falcon*. Threepio gazed out a narrow window and watched as Yavin Four became an increasingly distant dot among the stars.

"Better get buckled in back there," Solo's voice spoke over the *Falcon*'s comm. "We'll be making the jump to hyperspace in a few minutes."

"Dear, oh, dear," Threepio muttered. "I really do hate space travel." He turned to Artoo-Detoo. The astromech droid stood beside the holographic game table. Artoo had transformed the table into a workbench. He was nearly finished with Q-7N's repairs. The droid had needed quite a fix-up after the injuries it had sustained while helping Rebel forces in a battle on Yavin Four. It was quite an old model — a real challenge to restore.

"*Really*, Artoo!" Threepio said as he sat down beside the table and strapped himself to the seat. "I don't know why you're spending so much time working on that ancient droid."

Artoo emitted a rapid series of beeps.

"Yes, yes, yes," Threepio replied. "I *know* that the little fellow was of some help in capturing the Imperial captain on Yavin Four! But you don't *really* think that you can get the old thing to work again?"

"I'd app-app-appreciate," stammered the ball-like droid on the table, "if you duh-duh-didn't refer-rrrr to me as an-an-an 'old thing.'"

"Oh, sorry. I didn't know you could hear me." Threepio turned to Artoo. "Good work, Artoo-Detoo! I knew you could fix our new friend!"

Artoo whistled an electronic question to the tiny droid as he made an adjustment to Q-7N's vocabulator.

"Hmmm . . . yes, I think you've fixed it," Q-7N replied. "I can speak clearly again. Thank you, Artoo." Q-7N's photoreceptors rotated as the droid looked around. "Where are we?"

"We're in the central hold area of the *Millennium Falcon*, the ship owned by Han Solo," Threepio answered. "Master Solo was a smuggler, but now he and his copilot are members of the Rebel Alliance."

"I used to be owned by smugglers," said Q-7N, then corrected, "pirates, really. But that was a very long time ago." One of Q-7N's photoreceptors stared at Threepio and the small droid asked, "Are you and Artoo also Rebels?"

Q-7N's question caught Threepio off guard. The protocol droid had never thought of himself as a genuine member of the Rebellion. "Well, now that you mention it," Threepio began as his voice filled with pride, "I suppose we are!"

"Then I'm a Rebel too!" said Q-7N. "So tell me . . . what are we rebelling against?"

Threepio's head rocked back and he fixed his gaze on Q-7N. "Why, against the Empire, of course," said Threepio. "You know, like the stormtroopers that you fought on Yavin Four?"

"Oh!" exclaimed Q-7N. "Them!"

Threepio leaned close to Artoo and whispered, "Artoo? I think you might have missed one of Q-7N's memory circuits! How could anyone forget the Empire?"

Artoo's answer was lost to the noise of the *Falcon*'s engines as the battered stock light freighter thundered into hyperspace.

CHAPTER THREE

Admiral Termo sat at the desk in his private quarters on the Imperial Star Destroyer. Behind him, a small window was filled with a view of the planet Delrakkin. In front of the desk, Communications Officer Tix adjusted three switches on a compact holocomm, then attached two wires to one of the switches. After the wires were tied, Tix clipped one wire in half, clamped off one end, and rerouted the other to the Star Destroyer's computer. Termo watched the entire process with great interest.

"You're positive our ship's computer will not have any record of this transmission?" Termo inquired.

"Yes, sir," responded Tix.

"And you guarantee this transmission will not be intercepted and decoded?" asked Termo.

"There is always a possibility that a transmission may be intercepted on the HoloNet, sir," replied Tix. "But only the people at the destination frequency will be able to decode it."

"Good work, Tix," praised the Admiral. "Now leave."

Tix nodded and left the Admiral's room.

Termo cleared his throat. He stared into the plastic lens and activated the holocomm. Termo leaned forward and spoke into the microphone. "B90-478R. This is Admiral Termo, commanding officer of the Star Destroyer *Liquidator*, presently located in the Delrakkin system."

Above Termo's desk, a dark hologram blossomed from the desktop projector. Termo squinted at the glowing shape but could not see anything that resembled a face.

"Yes, Admiral Termo," a voice crackled from the hologram. "I have been expecting your transmission."

Termo didn't recognize the voice but thought it best to proceed. "The Death Star has not arrived at Delrakkin," said Termo. "I am waiting for orders from Grand Moff Tarkin."

There was a pause, and then the hologram began to laugh. There was something evil and sinister about the laughter. *If a deep cavern could laugh*, thought Termo, *it would sound like this*.

Termo stared fiercely at the hologram and said, "I fail to see any humor in this situation."

"No," replied the hologram. "You couldn't possibly. Because you don't *know*!"

The hologram shifted and Termo realized that the blob was a cloaked head. The cloak was pulled back and the head looked up. Termo found himself staring into a pair of cold, dead eyes.

"Grand Moff Tarkin is no longer with us," leered the hologram, and the face bared its rotten teeth. "The Death Star was destroyed!" At this, the hologram began to laugh again.

Termo didn't know what to say.

He had never before spoken with Emperor Palpatine.

The *Millennium Falcon* tore through hyperspace on its way to the Polith system and the planet Thyferra. Brilliant light flooded past the *Falcon*'s cockpit. The armored hull of the cruiser rattled against the pounding galactic storm.

"All right, everyone," Solo cautioned, "we're going to sublight."

"You're not going to arrive too close to Thyferra, are you?" Leia asked.

"Oh, I don't know," Solo remarked. "I was kind of thinking it would be great fun to just ram the *Falcon* right *into* the planet."

Leia shot an angry look at Solo. "I only meant that we should be especially cautious entering Thyferran space. We don't want to alert any Imperial ships that may be in the area."

"Well, thank you for stating the obvious, your Princessiveness," sniped an annoyed Solo. "Maybe *you'd* like to pilot the *Falcon*?"

"I'd sooner pilot a broken-down landspeeder," Leia proclaimed.

"Oh, yeah?" Solo asked. "Then why don't —"

"Will you two please stop fighting?" Luke interrupted. "It's really getting on my nerves."

Chewbacca looked over his shoulder and howled as he nodded in agreement with Luke.

"Some friend *you* are, furball," muttered Solo, nudging the hyperdrive compensator. The shimmering lights of hyperspace seemed to wash away as the *Falcon* entered realspace. The cockpit's windows were suddenly filled with a clear view of the surrounding stars.

"There it is," Solo said, pointing to a nearby planet. "Thyferra. It looks like a clear route from here." He turned to Leia. "Have you ever met Voralla Morbo?" he asked.

"No," Leia replied. "But I'm told she can often be found in a cantina near the spaceport at Zalxuc City. She keeps Docking Bay Seventy-two set aside for the Alliance."

"Does the cantina have a name?" Luke asked.

"It's called Morbo's Place," Leia replied.

"Huh. So she has her own cantina," Solo commented. "What do you think of *that*, Chewie?"

Chewbacca responded with several quick snorts that Solo recognized as the Wookiee's chuckle. Chewbacca liked cantinas. So did Solo.

"Punch it, pal," Solo ordered casually. The *Millennium Falcon* blasted toward Thyferra.

Minutes later, the *Falcon* hovered above the rooftops of Zalxuc City as it approached Docking Bay 72. Solo tapped several switches. A loud noise could be heard from below the *Falcon*.

"What are you doing?" Leia asked.

"I've detached the Y-wing from the hull," replied Solo, "and I'm using the *Falcon*'s tractor beam to lower it to that roof." Solo pointed to what appeared to be a sturdy metal rooftop. "We may need the Y-wing as a getaway ship, so we don't want it stuck to the *Falcon*."

Leia didn't say anything — Han knew she found it hard to admit he was right.

After the empty Y-wing was placed down safely, Solo landed the *Falcon* at Docking Bay 72. The *Falcon*'s ramp lowered to the ground, and the heroes of the Rebellion stepped out of the freighter. Q-7N floated near the droids.

"So, you said we're on Thyferra to find out about bacta shipments?" Q-7N asked.

"That's correct," Threepio replied.

"How exciting!" the floating droid exclaimed. Artoo beeped in agreement.

"How far away is Morbo's Place?" Luke asked Leia.

"It shouldn't be far," the Princess responded. "We'll have to ask around, but be careful. There may be Imperials here. If anyone asks, tell them we're from Corellia and we're hoping to line up some work in the bacta transport business."

"*You?* A *Corellian?!*" Solo scoffed at the Princess. "Now *that's* something I never would have — !"

"Stop where you are!" a steely voice commanded from behind the Rebels. Han reached for his blaster, but laser fire suddenly kicked up the dirt near his feet.

"Raise your hands and turn around! Slowly!" the voice ordered.

Q-7N dropped low behind Artoo-Detoo as the Rebels turned to face twenty-seven armed stormtroopers.

"Hi there, fellas," Solo grinned at the troopers. "You won't believe this, but we were *looking* for you guys!"

The lead trooper stepped forward and rammed the butt of his blaster rifle into Solo's stomach. Chewbacca roared at the trooper, but the Wookiee knew that he was out-gunned. Leia yelled as Solo dropped to the ground.

"Why are *you* yelling?" gasped Solo to Leia. "*I'm* the one who got hit!"

"Take them away," ordered the lead trooper. "Put each one in a separate cell!"

Luke and Chewbacca helped Han to his feet. "We've all got to try to escape!" Leia whispered. "If one of us can find Voralla Morbo, we can —"

"Quiet! If I hear another word, you will all be neutral-ized," yelled the lead trooper. He turned to the three troop-ers next to him. "Get this scum out of here!"

Q-7N moved out of range. But there was nothing to be done to save the Rebels.

"We're doomed!" Threepio whispered to Artoo. The troopers were closing in.

The Rebels were surrounded. The troopers' rifles were aimed to kill.

There was no way out.

Or was there?

MISSION
BRIEFING

Before you proceed, you must consult the Mission Guide for the rules of the STAR WARS MISSIONS. You must follow these rules at all times.

This is a Rebel mission.

You have been captured by stormtroopers on the planet Thyferra, the one planet in the galaxy that produces bacta. You have been separated from your fellow Rebels and placed in a cell.

Your goal is to escape from your cell, retrieve your weapons, and help your comrades escape. You must find Morbo's Place, a cantina near the spaceport — but be careful who you ask for directions. You must also learn all that you can about bacta production on Thyferra. The information may one day save your life.

You start this Mission with your MP total from your previous Mission, or 1000MP if this is your first Mission.

Choose your character. You can take no more than three weapons and three vehicles (including a Y-wing fighter). You can use Power twice in this Mission.

May the Force be with you.

YOUR MISSION:
ESCAPE
FROM
THYFERRA

The stormtroopers take away your weapons and separate you from the other Rebels. They know you will be easier to imprison if you are kept apart. One of the troopers puts your weapons in a duffel bag and slings the bag over his shoulder. Two other troopers keep their blaster rifles aimed at you.

The three troopers take you to an alley between two buildings, then through an arched doorway. You enter a dark hall, turn left down another corridor, then right. The hallway walls are made of baked clay and are cracked with age. The smell of decay hangs heavy in the air.

You turn several more times, and you try to remember each turn. If you're going to escape, you'll need to know the way back to Docking Bay 72.

You arrive at a wooden door. One of the troopers unlocks the door and pulls it open to reveal a small cell. You are pushed inside and the door is locked behind you.

The cell is illuminated by a single glow rod that hangs from the ceiling. You search every corner of the chamber. There doesn't appear to be any hidden camera, but a small comm speaker is built into the wall near the door.

Parts of the outer wall have crumbled away, but the inner wall is thick. There's no way you'll be able to tunnel out of here.

You press your weight against the door. Although it is heavy, the frame appears to be brittle. If you brace yourself, one good kick might knock the door down.

There's a muffled sound from the hallway. You press your ear to the door and listen carefully.

"You two stay here," says one stormtrooper. "I'm going

back to Docking Bay Seventy-two to report to squad leader. If the prisoner tries to escape, shoot."

You hear footsteps crunching on the ground, walking away. That leaves two troopers outside the cell door. You're unarmed, but you've got one big advantage over the stormtroopers: you're smart.

"Unnnnngh!" you groan loudly.

"Quiet!" one of the two troopers orders.

"I can't reach your arm!" you yell to the empty air above you. "Try again!"

"What do you think is going on in there?" one trooper asks.

"Sounds like someone's helping the prisoner escape!" the other responds. "We'd better open the door!"

You hear one of the troopers trying to open the lock. He must be right on the other side of the door. That's exactly where you want him.

You brace yourself. It's time to make your move.

To kick down the door and knock out the first storm-trooper: Your strength# +1 is your confront#. Roll the 6-dice to kick down the door.

> *If your confront# is equal to or more than your roll#,* add the difference to your Mission Point (MP) total and proceed to combat the second trooper (below).

> *If your confront# is less than your roll#,* subtract the difference from your MP total. Add +1 to your confront# and repeat this confront with your new confront# until you have kicked down the door and knocked out

the first trooper. Once you have defeated the first trooper, you may proceed to combat the second trooper (below).

To combat the second stormtrooper: Add your strength# to your skill# +3 for your confront#. Roll the 12-dice to throw a punch at the stormtrooper.

If your confront# is equal to or more than your roll#, add the difference to your MP total.

If your confront# is less than your roll#, subtract the difference from your MP total and repeat this confront until you have knocked out the stormtrooper.

Once you have defeated the second stormtrooper, add 10MP to your MP total. You may now proceed to retrieve your weapons.

You're in luck. The duffel bag that contains your weapons is sitting on the ground near one of the fallen troopers. You grab your weapons and run down the hall.

As you come around a corner, a metal object hits the top of your head. You duck back into the hallway and check for a bruise. No real harm done. But what hit you?

"Are you all right?" Q-7N asks. The floating droid drops down in front of your face. "I didn't mean to fly into you."

"How did you get away from the troopers?" you ask.

"As soon as the stormtroopers appeared, I dropped low to the ground," the droid replies. "I stuck close to everyone's feet, then managed to duck into a hole in the wall. I'm so small, nobody even noticed. I came this way because I wanted to try and help you escape, but it looks like you've already managed that on your own!"

"Did you see where the troopers took everyone else?" you ask.

"I'm afraid not," Q-7N responds.

"Those stormtroopers were *waiting* for us at the docking bay," you comment. "Almost like they *knew* we were coming! But *how*?!"

Blaster fire tears at the wall near your head. You duck and turn to see the third stormtrooper, the one who left your cell area to report to his squad leader. The trooper must have heard you escape and turned back. Without hesitating, you decide to fight. You can't be captured again.

You can choose to combat the stormtrooper with your fists or with a weapon.

To combat the stormtrooper with your fists: Add your strength# to your skill# +3 for your confront#. Roll the 12-dice to fight the stormtrooper.

If your confront# is equal to or more than your roll#, add the difference to your MP total and proceed.

If your confront# is less than your roll#, subtract the difference from your MP total. Add +1 to your confront# and repeat this confront with your new confront# until you have defeated the trooper.

To combat the stormtrooper with a weapon: Choose your weapon. Add your weaponry# to your weapon's mid-range# +2 for your confront#. Roll the 12-dice to combat the trooper.

> *If your confront# is equal to or more than your roll#,* add the difference to your MP total and proceed.

> *If your confront# is less than your roll#,* subtract the difference from your MP total. Now add +4 for your confront# for your new confront#. Roll the 12-dice again to continue your combat with the trooper.

>> *If your new confront# is equal to or more than your roll#,* add the difference to your MP total and proceed.

>> *If your new confront# is less than your roll#,* subtract the difference from your MP total. Repeat this confront with your new confront# until you have defeated the trooper. Then you may proceed.

Q-7N hovers next to you as you run to the fallen stormtrooper. "That was close!" it exclaims. The droid watches as you remove the stormtrooper's helmet, then asks, "What are you doing?"

"I'm going to put on his armor," you reply. "I'll be able to move more easily through this place if I'm disguised as a stormtrooper."

"Well, then it's a good thing I ran into you when I did," Q-7N comments as you put on the armor. "Otherwise, I would have thought you were a real stormtrooper!"

"Let's hope my friends don't make that mistake!" you

declare as you strap the stormtrooper's belt around your waist. "Do you know the way out of here?"

"Why, yes," replies the droid. "I'm quite good at mazes. After all, I lived in that fortress on Yavin Four —"

"I know all that, Q-7N!" you interrupt. "Let's get moving!"

You follow Q-7N and make a number of turns until you reach a stairway that leads down to a low metal door. Q-7N stops and hangs in the air in front of the stairway. "This door looks promising!" it says.

"What do you mean?" you ask. "I don't remember walking through that door. I don't even remember walking *past* it!"

"According to my topographic sensors," replies Q-7N, "this door is a shortcut to Docking Bay Seventy-two."

"But it looks like this door leads to a basement," you observe.

"I assure you," states Q-7N, "we'll get there faster if we go this way."

"Then let's take it," you say as you descend the stairs. You press your hand against the door activator and the metal door slides into the wall. You lower your head and enter the doorway, Q-7N at your side.

When you look up, you find yourself in a long, narrow room filled with computer equipment. There's a door at the far end of the room, but there's a problem. Two Imperial technicians are seated at their computer terminals. They look up at you. One of them rises from his seat.

"What are you doing down here?" asks the standing technician. "Why aren't you at your post?"

"I, um, took a wrong turn," you mumble. A whirring air conditioner nearly drowns you out.

The other technician gets to his feet. "What kind of a droid is that?" he asks. Both men carry laser pistols.

You can choose to mislead the technicians or fight. If you choose to fight, you can fight the technicians all at once or one at a time.

To mislead (without Power): You tell the technician you are looking for a droid repair shop for Q-7N. Your charm# +3 is your confront#. Roll the 12-dice to evade the two Imperial technicians.

> *If your confront# is equal to or more than your roll#,* add 10MP to your MP total and proceed to the door at the end of the office.

> *If your confront# is lower than your roll#,* subtract the difference from your MP total. The technicians do not believe that you're looking for a droid repair shop. You must combat the technicians (below).

To lie (using Power)*: You tell the technicians you are on your way to a droid repair shop with Q-7N. Choose your Persuasion Power. Add your stealth# to your Power's low-resist# for your confront#. Roll the 6-dice to evade the technicians.

> *If your confront# is equal to or more than your roll#,* add the difference to your MP total and proceed.

If your confront# is lower than your roll#, subtract the difference from your MP total. The technicians realize you are lying. You must combat the technicians (below).

*Note: This counts as one of two Power uses you are allowed in this Mission.

To combat both technicians at once: Add your weaponry# to your weapon's close-range# for your confront#. Roll the 12-dice to shoot the air conditioner, which will explode and knock out the technicians.

If your confront# is equal to or more than your roll#, add 7MP to your MP total and proceed to the door at the end of the office.

If your confront# is lower than your roll#, subtract the difference from your MP total. Now double your confront# for your new confront#. Roll the 12-dice again to continue to combat the technicians.

If your new confront# is equal to or more than your roll#, add the difference to your MP total and proceed to the door.

If your new confront# is less than your roll#, subtract the difference from your MP total. You have missed the air conditioner and must now combat the technicians one at a time (below).

To combat one technician at a time: Add your weaponry# to your weapon's mid-range# for your confront#. Roll the 6-dice to combat the first technician.

If your confront# is equal to or more than your roll#, add the difference to your MP total and proceed to combat the second technician, using the same confront equation.

If your confront# is less than your roll#, subtract the difference from your MP total and repeat this confront. Once you have defeated the first technician, repeat this confront to combat the second technician, using the same confront equation.

Once you have defeated the second technician, add 30MP to your MP total (50MP for Advanced Level players). You may proceed to the door at the end of the room.

As you walk to the far end of the office, you cast a glance at Q-7N.

"What are you looking at?" asks the floating droid.

"You've got a funny way of choosing shortcuts," you respond.

"How could I have known there would be anyone down here?" Q-7N argues. "Besides, you handled those two quite well."

You open the door and find yourself in another hallway. The hall looks familiar. Q-7N was right about the shortcut after all.

Q-7N leads you through the hall until you emerge under the arched doorway and into the alley. "I remember it from here," you say to the floating droid. "Docking Bay Seventy-two is just around this corner."

"What if more Imperials question you?" Q-7N asks.

You raise a finger and tap it against your helmet. "*This* trooper was on his way to report to the squad leader at the docking bay. Maybe I can get the leader to tell me how they knew where to find us and where our friends are being held."

At the docking bay, a dozen stormtroopers surround the *Millennium Falcon*. You turn your helmeted head to Q-7N. "Stay here, and keep out of sight. If something happens, do whatever you can to find the other Rebels."

"Hurry back," Q-7N encourages. The droid rises up to a gutter along the roof. From this position, it will have a good view of your encounter with the Imperial squad leader.

The squad leader looks up as you approach. You try to keep calm, knowing that you look like every other stormtrooper. But there are a lot of other troopers. If this turns into a fight, you might not be able to win.

"What kept you?" asks the squad leader.

"The prisoner started to talk," you reply. You point to the *Falcon*. "The prisoner said that they bought this ship a few days ago."

"What's your point, soldier?" the squad leader barks. "Our orders are to detain *any* ship that lands in this docking bay! The last three ships to arrive at this docking bay were supplying bacta to the Rebel Alliance!"

"Yes, sir," you respond. Now you know that the troopers weren't trying to capture the *Falcon* in particular. They just got lucky. You look toward the Corellian freighter. "Still, I thought we might question the other prisoners. Maybe we can find out if they all tell the same story. If one of them says something different, we'll know they're lying."

The squad leader tilts his helmet to one side. He is trying to think, but isn't very good at it.

"Good idea," he says. "Let's go ask them." He starts to walk away from the *Falcon*. You follow.

"Sir!" calls a stormtrooper to the squad leader. The stormtrooper carries a data pad. "I ran a check on this freighter!" He's referring to the *Falcon*. "According to my data pad, this freighter matches the description of a ship that escaped Imperial forces on Tatooine. If the information checks out, Grand Moff Tarkin himself will want to know about this ship!"

Tatooine? you think. *That was days ago. And Grand Moff Tarkin perished on the Death Star!* Suddenly, you realize that the news of the Death Star's destruction has not yet reached Thyferra.

The information on the data pad could cost the lives of your friends and fellow Rebels. You can't let the stormtrooper give this information to anyone else. You'll have to fight the squad leader and this trooper, or you'll have to try to talk the stormtrooper into giving the pad to you.

To convince the stormtrooper to give you the data pad (without Power): Your charm# +1 is your confront#. Roll the 6-dice to talk your way out of this one.

> *If your confront# is equal to or more than your roll#,* add the difference to your MP total. You now have the data pad. The squad leader and stormtrooper are satisfied, and leave you to proceed.

If your confront# is less than your roll#, subtract the difference from your MP total. The squad leader and stormtrooper suspect you are an impostor. You must fight them (below).

To convince the stormtrooper to give you the data pad (using Power)*: Choose your Persuasion Power. Use your charm# + your Power's low-resist# + your Jedi# as your confront#. Roll the 6-dice to talk your way out of this one.

If your confront# is equal to or more than your roll#, add the difference to your MP total. You now have the data pad. The squad leader and stormtrooper are satisfied, and leave you to proceed.

If your confront# is less than your roll#, subtract the difference from your MP total. The squad leader and stormtrooper suspect you are an impostor. You must fight them (below).

*Note: This counts as one of two Power uses you are allowed in this Mission.

To combat the squad leader: Choose your weapon. Add your weaponry# to your weapon's close-range# +1 for your confront#. Roll the 6-dice to shoot the squad leader.

If your confront# is equal to or more than your roll#, add the difference to your MP total. You may now proceed to combat the stormtrooper (below).

If your confront# is less than your roll#, subtract the difference from your MP total. Repeat this confront until you have defeated the squad leader. Once you have defeated the squad leader, proceed to combat the stormtrooper (below).

To combat the stormtrooper: Add your weaponry# to your weapon's close-range# +2 for your confront#. Roll the 12-dice to shoot the stormtrooper.

If your confront# is equal to or more than your roll#, add the difference to your MP total and proceed, hiding the bodies of the stormtrooper and the squad leader, so no one else can see them.

If your confront# is less than your roll#, subtract the difference from your MP total. Add +3 to your confront# for your new confront#. Roll the 12-dice to shoot again.

If your new confront# is equal to or more than your roll#, you may proceed, hiding the bodies of the stormtrooper and squad leader, so no one else can see them.

If your new confront# is less than your roll#, subtract the difference from your MP total and repeat this confront until you have defeated the stormtrooper.

The squad leader and the stormtrooper are no longer a problem. But you have attracted the attention of the other stormtroopers, who are wondering why you have the data pad.

"You there!" yells one trooper. "Stop where you are!" The trooper is running toward you. His blaster rifle is drawn and ready to fire. The other troopers watch from a distance. They're not sure what to do.

There are ten stormtroopers in the docking bay. They're all spread out around the *Falcon*. You know you can't fight them all and win. But because you're wearing the uniform of a stormtrooper, you may be able to talk your way out of this with the approaching trooper.

Choose to talk your way out of this or combat the approaching stormtrooper.

To talk your way out (without Power): If you talked your way out of the last confront, your charm# +2 is your confront#. If you had to combat in the last confront, your charm# is your confront#. Roll the 6-dice to evade the stormtrooper.

> *If your confront# is equal to or more than your roll#*, add the difference to your MP total. The trooper believes that you are a fellow stormtrooper and you may leave the docking bay.

> *If your confront# is lower than your roll#*, subtract the difference from your MP total. The trooper doesn't believe you and you will have to combat him (below).

To talk your way out (using Power)*: Choose your Persuasion or your Evasion Power. Your stealth# + your Power's low-resist# + your Jedi# is your confront#. Roll the 6-dice to talk your way out of this one.

If your confront# is equal to or more than your roll#, add the difference to your MP total. You may leave the docking bay.

If your confront# is less than your roll#, subtract the difference from your MP total. The trooper doesn't believe you and you have no choice but to fight (below).

*Note: This counts as one of two Power uses you are allowed in this Mission.

To combat the stormtrooper: Choose your weapon. Add your weaponry# to your weapon's mid-range# +4 for your confront#. Roll the 12-dice to combat the stormtrooper.

If your confront# is equal to or more than your roll#, add the difference to your MP total and proceed.

If your confront# is lower than your roll#, subtract the difference from your MP total and repeat this confront, adding +2 to your confront# for your new confront#. Once you have defeated the stormtrooper, you may proceed.

"Follow me!" calls a voice from above. You look up to see Q-7N, who hovers by a metal gutter. "Climb this gutter and you can make it to the roof!"

To climb to the roof: Add your strength# to your stealth# for your confront#. Roll the 6-dice to climb hand-over-hand up the gutter.

If your confront# is equal to or more than your roll#, add the difference to your MP total and proceed.

If your confront# is lower than your roll#, subtract the difference from your MP total. Using the same equation, repeat this confront until you have reached the rooftop. Once you're on the roof, you may proceed.

"Where do we go from here?" you ask.
"To the Y-wing!" Q-7N replies. "Over there!"
On a nearby rooftop, the Y-wing starfighter rests where it was left by the *Falcon*.
To reach the Y-wing, you'll have to run and make a broad jump from one roof to the next.

To run and jump: Add your strength# to your stealth# +2 for your confront#. Roll the 12-dice to make the jump.

If your confront# is equal to or more than your roll#, add the difference to your MP total and proceed.

If your confront# is lower than your roll#, subtract the difference from your MP total. You tried to jump but didn't quite make it. You're dangling from the gutter by your fingertips and must pull yourself up (below).

To pull yourself up: Your strength# +2 is your confront#. Roll the 6-dice to swing your body up onto the roof.

If your confront# is equal to or more than your roll#, add the difference to your MP total and proceed.

If your confront# is lower than your roll#, subtract the difference from your MP total. Using the same equation, repeat this confront until you are standing on the rooftop. Once you're up, you may proceed.

You run to the Y-wing and climb into the cockpit. Q-7N flies into the seat behind you.

"Are you sure you know how to fly this ship?" it asks.

"There's a first time for everything," you reply. "Hang on!"

To fly the Y-wing: Use your vehicle card. Add your vehicle's distance# to your vehicle's speed#+1 for your confront#. Roll the 6-dice to launch the Y-wing starfighter off the roof.

If your confront# is equal to or more than your roll#, add the difference to your MP total and proceed.

If your confront# is lower than your roll#, subtract the difference from your MP total. Repeat the confront using the same confront# until you have successfully launched the Y-wing.

"How far are we going?" Q-7N asks. "How are we going to rescue our friends?"

"Don't worry," you reply. "I'm only flying a short distance away. I just want to put some space between us and the stormtroopers. We'll still be within walking distance of Docking Bay Seventy-two."

Gazing down at the spaceport below, you circle until

you see a crowded docking area. There are many small ships that are leaving or docking. You point to it and say, "We should be able to land there without drawing too much attention."

"If you don't want any attention, you might want to take off your stormtrooper uniform!" Q-7N points out.

"You're right," you admit as you take off your helmet. "No wonder I'm so uncomfortable."

You dock the Y-wing, then take off the armor and leave it in the backseat. Q-7N stays close to your side as you step away from the dock and lose yourself in a crowd of bizarre creatures.

"Where do we go from here?" Q-7N asks.

"We'll have to try and find Voralla Morbo at her cantina," you reply. "If she's been loyal to the Rebellion in the past, maybe she can help us."

A Kubaz stands against the wall, chewing on a toothpick. The Kubaz is wearing goggles to protect his large, sensitive eyes from any harsh light. Instead of a nose, the Kubaz has a short trunk. The trunk lifts and twists to remove the toothpick from his mouth.

"Do you think that Kubaz might be helpful?" you ask Q-7N.

"I don't know about him," replies the floating droid. "He looks suspicious!"

"I'll risk it," you reply. You walk to the Kubaz and smile. "Excuse me, but I'm looking for a cantina named Morbo's Place. Can you point me in the right direction?"

The Kubaz stares down at you. You'll have to try harder than that.

To get help from the Kubaz (without Power): Your charm# +1 is your confront#. Roll the 6-dice to receive directions from the Kubaz.

> *If your confront# is equal to or more than your roll#,* add the difference to your MP total and proceed.

> *If your confront# is less than your roll#,* subtract the difference from your MP total. The Kubaz is rubbing his fingers together and expects you to pay him for the information. Subtract another 5MP from your MP total. You have paid for this confront, and you may now proceed.

To get help from the Kubaz (using Power)*: Choose your Persuasion Power. Your charm# + your Power's low-resist# + your Jedi# is your confront#. Roll the 6-dice to talk your way out of this one.

> *If your confront# is equal to or more than your roll#,* add the difference to your MP total and proceed.

> *If your confront# is less than your roll#,* subtract the difference from your MP total. The Kubaz is rubbing his fingers together and expects you to pay him for the information. Subtract another 5MP from your MP total. You have paid for this confront, and you may now proceed.

*Note: This counts as one of two Power uses you are allowed in this Mission.

"So, you'll give me the directions?" you ask.

"I can do better than that, spacer," responds the Kubaz, looking down his trunk at you. "I was on my way there myself. I'd be happy to escort you. It's not far."

Several minutes later, you arrive at a cantina. It's a seedy place, dark and gloomy even from the outside. The building looks as though it might fall apart at any moment.

"Are you sure this is the right cantina?" you ask the Kubaz.

"Sure," the Kubaz replies. "Come on in. I know the owner here. I'll introduce you."

"Well, okay," you say. Next to the cantina door, there's a sign: NO DROIDS ALLOWED.

"I think I'll wait out here," Q-7N says.

"Good idea," you mumble. "Try and stay out of trouble." The Kubaz steps through the doorway and you follow.

Several aliens look up at you as you enter. They remain quiet. One of the aliens has five red eyes. He smiles and nods his enormous head as you walk to the counter.

The Kubaz sits down and points to the stool next to him. "Have a seat," he says. "Relax. You're among friends here."

A tall Devaronian appears on the other side of the counter. The horns that come out of his head nearly scrape the ceiling. "Well, hello," says the Devaronian to the Kubaz. "I see you've brought a guest." The Devaronian turns to face you.

"Hello," you respond to the horned creature. "I was wondering if I could speak to the owner of this place."

The Devaronian smiles. He has many sharp teeth. "You're looking at him," he states. "I am the owner of this cantina."

"But I thought that Morbo's Place was owned by a woman," you mention as you cast a glance at the Kubaz. The Kubaz won't look at you.

"You're correct," says the Devaronian. "Voralla Morbo does own Morbo's Place. The problem is . . . this isn't Morbo's Place!"

With one swift motion, the Devaronian pulls a switch and a trapdoor opens beneath your stool. You yell as you fall through the trapdoor and find yourself tumbling down a metal slide.

At the bottom of the slide, you land with a smash upon a cold stone floor. As you struggle to stand up, you hear a grunting sound and realize you are not alone. From a nearby corner in the room, a Gamorrean stares down at you. The pig-faced brute wears heavy armor and carries a menacing axe. At the sight of you, drool begins to flow from the corners of his upturned mouth, making his tusks glisten. Beyond the Gamorrean, you see a high wooden door.

You try to run for the door, but the Gamorrean steps in your way. He snorts at you as he raises his axe.

You can't talk your way out of this one.

You can choose to combat the Gamorrean with your fists or with a weapon.

To combat the Gamorrean with your fists: Add your strength# to your stealth# +2 for your confront#. Roll the 12-dice to throw a devastating punch at the Gamorrean.

If your confront# is equal to or more than your roll#, add 15MP to your MP total and proceed.

If your confront# is less than your roll#, subtract the difference from your MP total. This Gamorrean is too tough for you. You'll have to use your weapon (below).

To combat the Gamorrean with your weapon: Choose your weapon. Add your weapon# to your weaponry's close-range# +1 for your confront#. Roll the 12-dice to blast the Gamorrean out of his boots.

If your confront# is equal to or more than your roll#, add the difference to your MP total and proceed.

If your confront# is less than your roll#, subtract the difference from your MP total. Add +3 to your confront# for your new confront#. Roll the 12-dice to shoot again.

If your new confront# is equal to or more than your roll#, you may proceed.

If your new confront# is less than your roll#, subtract the difference from your MP total and repeat this confront using the same new confront# until you have defeated the Gamorrean.

Stopping the Gamorrean was quite an achievement. Add 10MP to your MP total (25MP for Advanced Level players).

You're stepping over the Gamorrean's body when you hear a familiar voice call behind you, "Wait for me!"

"Q-7N?!" you exclaim. "How did you get down here?"

"When I heard you yell, I flew inside the cantina," replies the droid. "The creatures were all laughing. I think they planned on robbing you! Then I saw the open trapdoor and raced down to find you!"

"You're a brave little droid, Q-7N. Those guys upstairs may have planned something worse than robbing me. Some aliens are known to trap wandering spacers, then use them for slave labor!"

Q-7N aims a photoreceptor at the floor and examines the Gamorrean. "What happened to this fellow?"

"What do you think?" you reply. "Come on! We have to get out of here!"

You go to the door, but it's locked.

To open the door, you can choose to hotwire the lock, kick the door down, or fire your weapon at the lock. You must choose now.

To hotwire the lock: Your skill# +1 is your confront#. Roll the 6-dice to hotwire the lock.

If your confront# is equal to or more than your roll#, add the difference to your MP total and proceed.

If your confront# is less than your roll#, subtract the difference from your MP total. There's no way you can hotwire this lock, so you must either kick the door down or blast the lock off (below).

To kick the door down: Your strength# +1 is your confront#. Roll the 6-dice to launch a powerful kick at the door.

If your confront# is equal to or more than your roll#, add the difference to your MP total and proceed.

If your confront# is less than your roll#, subtract the difference from your MP total. You're probably just worn out from your battle with the Gamorrean. Proceed to blast the lock off (below), or try to hotwire the lock (above).

To blast the lock off: Your weaponry# + your weapon's close-range# is your confront#. Roll the 6-dice to take a shot at the lock.

If your confront# is equal to or more than your roll#, add the difference to your MP total and proceed.

If your confront# is less than your roll#, subtract the difference from your MP total. Now double your confront# for your new confront#. Roll the 12-dice to fire another blast at the stubborn lock.

If your new confront# is equal to or more than your roll#, you may proceed.

If your new confront# is less than your roll#, subtract the difference from your MP total. Repeat this confront with your new confront# until you have shattered the lock. You may then proceed through the doorway.

Q-7N follows you through the doorway and into a tunnel. At the far end of the tunnel, another Gamorrean guard looks up from his post. He grunts angrily at the sight of you.

"He's probably wondering where his friend is," you mutter to Q-7N.

Q-7N notices that the Gamorrean is reaching for something. "Stop him!" cries the droid. "He's trying to pull a lever!"

Choose your weapon to shoot the Gamorrean.

To shoot the Gamorrean: Add your weaponry# to your weapon's far-range# for your confront#. Roll the 12-dice to fire a blast at the dastardly beast.

If your confront# is equal to or more than your roll#, add the difference to your MP total and proceed.

If your confront# is less than your roll#, subtract the difference from your MP total. Now double your confront# for your new confront#. Roll the 12-dice again to fire another shot at the Gamorrean.

If your new confront# is equal to or more than your roll#, you may proceed.

If your new confront# is less than your roll#, subtract the difference from your MP total. Repeat this confront with your new confront# until you have neutralized the Gamorrean. Then you may proceed.

As the Gamorrean falls, his arm strikes the lever.

"Step back!" Q-7N yells, and you quickly jump backward. Suddenly, the tunnel floor falls away in front of you. You stand on the broken ledge, gazing down into the pit in front of you. Dozens of long metal spikes poke up from the pit.

"How did you know the floor was rigged?"

"I wasn't certain, but I knew *something* bad would happen when he pulled that lever!" Q-7N looks up to the tunnel ceiling. Two glow rods dangle along the length of the tunnel. "Since the floor is rigged, you might want to swing from one glow rod to the next until you reach the other side of the tunnel," the droid suggests.

"It'll be faster if I just run and jump over this pit," you reply.

"You wouldn't dare!" Q-7N challenges.

You must choose how you are going to cross the pit. You can either swing from one glow rod to the next or attempt a single leap. Choose now, then proceed.

To swing from the glow rods: Add your strength# to your skill# for your confront#. Roll the 6-dice to leap and grab the first glow rod.

> If your confront# is equal to or more than your roll#, you may proceed to the second glow rod, using the same confront equation. Once you have reached the second glow rod, you may proceed.

> If your confront# is less than your roll#, subtract the difference from your MP total and repeat this confront. Once you have grasped the first glow rod, repeat this confront to reach the second glow rod. Once you have reached the second glow rod, you may proceed.

To leap over the pit: Add your skill# to your strength# +2 for your confront#. Roll the 12-dice to run and leap the pit in a single bound.

If your confront# is equal to or more than your roll#, you've made the leap. Add the difference to your MP total and proceed.

If your confront# is lower than your roll#, subtract the difference from your MP total and repeat this confront, adding +2 to your confront# for your new confront#. Once you have leaped the pit, you may proceed.

Once you have crossed the pit, add 20MP to your MP total.

After you reach the other side of the pit, Q-7N glides through the air and arrives by your side.

"Too bad you couldn't just fly over," remarks the droid.

"One of these days," you gasp, "you'll have to teach me."

An open doorway leads you to a spiral staircase. Q-7N stays close to your head as you climb the stone steps. At the top of the stairway, you reach another door. It appears to be unlocked.

"What do you think is on the other side?" you ask Q-7N.

"According to my topography sensors," says the droid, "the tunnel led us away from the cantina, but we've risen into a building next door to the cantina."

You push the door open and find yourself in a murky room. The room is illuminated by a heavy bracket of glow rods hanging from the ceiling. You see another doorway and step toward it. You've almost reached the doorway when you spy a triangular gametable under the bracket of glow rods. At the gametable, three aliens look up from their card game.

Only one alien appears familiar. He's a reptiloid Brubb, and his dusty yellow, ridged eyes gleam against his dark skin. He wears a black, sleeveless tunic that reveals the long, lean muscles on his scale-covered arms.

The second alien is a chubby fellow. Instead of a head, three stalks seem to grow out of his neck. At the end of each stalk is a bloodshot, purple eyeball.

The third alien has a bulbous head and does not appear to have any eyes at all. In one of his six tentacles, he holds his cards close to a small hole in the middle of his head. He has a massive lower body with four powerful legs. Instead of sitting in a chair, he squats on the floor beside the table.

"Hey!" shouts the Brubb. "This is a private game!"

The second alien squints all three of his eyes at you and says, "Wait a minute . . . Where are the Guff twins?"

"He must mean the two Gamorreans!" whispers Q-7N.

The third alien throws down his cards and leaps to his four feet. "What's the matter, spacer?" he snarls. "Droid got your tongue?"

To leave this room, you can choose to talk or fight your way out. To fight, you can choose all at once or one at a time.

To talk your way out (without Power): Your charm# +1 is your confront#. Roll the 6-dice to leave this room without any difficulty.

If your confront# is equal to or more than your roll#, add the difference to your MP total. The stupid aliens believe your tale that you are a relative of the Guff twins, and you may proceed.

If your confront# is less than your roll#, subtract the difference from your MP total. The card players do not believe you when you tell them that you are the Guff twins' second cousin. Now you'll have to fight the aliens (choose from below).

To talk your way out (using Power)*: Choose your Persuasion Power. Your charm# + your Power's low-resist# + your Jedi# is your confront#. Roll the 6-dice to talk your way out of this one.

If your confront# is equal to or more than your roll#, add the difference to your MP total. The aliens believe your tale that you are a relative of the Guff twins, and you may proceed.

If your confront# is less than your roll#, subtract the difference from your MP total. The card players do not believe you. Now you'll have to fight (below).

Note: This counts as one of two Power uses you are allowed in this Mission.

To fight the aliens all at once: Choose your weapon. Add your weaponry# to your weapon's mid-range# +2 for your confront#. Roll the 12-dice to shoot the heavy glow rod bracket that hangs above the aliens.

If your confront# is equal to or more than your roll#, add the difference to your MP total. The bracket has crashed down upon the aliens and you may proceed.

If your confront# is less than your roll#, subtract the difference from your MP total. The aliens can't believe you missed that shot and they leap away from the table. Now you'll have to fight them one at a time.

To fight the aliens one at a time: Choose your weapon. Add your weaponry# to your weapon's mid-range# +1 for your confront#. Roll the 6-dice to begin shooting.

If your confront# is equal to or more than your roll#, add the difference to your MP total. You may proceed to combat the second alien, using the same confront equation.

If your confront# is less than your roll#, subtract the difference from your MP total and repeat this confront. Once you have defeated the first alien, repeat this confront with the same confront# to combat the second alien.

After you defeat the second alien, you may proceed to combat the third alien, using the same confront equation. When the third alien is defeated, you may proceed.

No matter how you pulled it off, it wasn't easy. Add 50MP to your MP total (75 for Advanced Level players).

"Good show," praises Q-7N. "I'm glad I'm on your side."

"Thanks," you reply. "You say we're next door to the cantina?" you ask the floating droid.

"I think so," replies Q-7N.

"Thank goodness," you say. You place your hand on the door activator and the door slides open.

But the door does not open to the outside world. Instead, you find yourself in a large stockroom. There is dirt on the floor. Boxes are piled everywhere.

"This isn't outside at all!" declares Q-7N. "It looks like some kind of warehouse."

"Yeah, but what are they warehousing?" you ask. "This place is a mess."

"What are you doing in here?!" yells a voice to your left. You turn to see that the speaker is a green-skinned Rodian standing on a catwalk, glaring down at you with his large, multifaceted eyes. Another Rodian stands beside him, and they appear to be identical. Their tapirlike snouts begin to twitch, and you wonder whether they picked up your scent as you entered the warehouse. They are both outfitted in matching orange jumpsuits and carry holstered blasters. Below the Rodians, a large vat of chemicals stands bubbling.

"Hey!" exclaims the other Rodian. "Why aren't any of the guards with him?" The two Rodians reach for their blasters with their suction-cup-tipped fingers.

You can choose to combat both Rodians at once, or one at a time.

To combat both Rodians at once: Choose your weapon. Add your weaponry# to your weapon's far-range# for your confront#. Roll the 6-dice to shoot at the main support of the catwalk.

>If your confront# is equal to or more than your roll#, add the difference to your MP total. The main support explodes and the catwalk crashes. You may now proceed.

>If your confront# is lower than your roll#, subtract the difference from your MP total. You have missed the support and must now combat the Rodians one at a time.

To combat one Rodian at a time: Choose your weapon. Add your weaponry# to your weapon's far-range# for your confront#. Roll the 6-dice to shoot at the first Rodian.

>If your confront# is equal to or more than your roll#, add the difference to your MP total. Repeat the confront to combat the second Rodian. Once you have defeated the two Rodians, you may proceed.

>If your confront# is lower than your roll#, subtract the difference from your MP total and repeat this confront, adding +1 to your confront# for your new confront#. Once you have defeated the first Rodian, repeat this confront with the same confront# to combat the second Rodian.

The two Rodians topple off the catwalk and into the vat with a great splash.

"Try and find a way out of here," you order Q-7N. "I'm going to look around and see what sort of operation this is."

The crates open easily enough. Inside one, you find various packaged ingredients. A second crate appears to be filled with soil, but as you sift through it, you find that there are strange-looking plants underneath.

"I couldn't find any way out," announces Q-7N, peering into the crates. "Did you find out what they're making here?"

"I'm not sure," you say. "I'm hardly a chemist, but I think —"

A shuffling noise causes you to stop talking and listen. You draw your blaster and inch your way around a nearby crate. Behind the crate, you find a shivering figure huddled on the floor.

"Please don't shoot us!" cries the insectoid figure as its two three-fingered hands try to cover its triangular face. "We are not violent!"

"Don't worry," you say as you lower your weapon. "I'm not going to shoot you. What's your name?"

"We are called Plurra," answers the alien.

"Why does this creature refer to itself as 'us' and 'we?'" asks Q-7N.

"Because it's a Vratix," you reply. "The Vratix share a collective mind. Instead of 'I,' they say 'we.'"

"You know of the Vratix?" Plurra asks. "You will help us escape?"

"I'll try," you answer. "But first, maybe you can help me. Can you tell me what's in these crates?"

The Vratix rises onto its four legs and moves to the crates. It points to the first one. "This one contains the ingredients for *kavam*. The other contains the plant *alazhi*."

"What does that mean?" Q-7N asks.

"When kavam is combined with alazhi," the Vratix explains, "it produces *bacta!*" Plurra's large compound eyes seem to have a life of their own. They dart in many different directions at once. "The Vratix is known for making the best bacta. That is why we are enslaved here!"

"How horrible!" Q-7N gasps.

"Our only hope," says Plurra, "is that the bacta we produce might help someone who needs it —"

Plurra is interrupted by sudden blaster fire that strikes the crates. The Vratix has powerful legs and leaps out of the range of fire. You dive behind one of the crates and Q-7N rises rapidly toward the ceiling.

"It's the two aliens from the catwalk!" Q-7N warns.

"The Rodians?" you yell as more blaster fire rips into the wall behind your head. "But I took care of those guys!"

"That's what you think!" screams one Rodian as he fires another shot in your direction and moves in front of a stack of crates. "You almost took care of us permanently, but we landed in a vat of bacta!"

"Yeah," hollers the second Rodian, "and now we're all healed!"

"Thanks for explaining it to me," you mutter as you draw your weapon and leap out from behind the crate.

You must battle the two Rodians again. You can choose to combat both Rodians at once or one at a time.

To combat both Rodians at once: Choose your weapon. Add your weaponry# to your weapon's close-range# for your confront#. Roll the 6-dice to shoot at a stack of nearby crates.

If your confront# is equal to or more than your roll#, add the difference to your MP total. The stack of crates tumbles down and crushes the Rodians. You may now proceed.

If your confront# is lower than your roll#, subtract the difference from your MP total. You have missed the stack of crates and must now combat the Rodians one at a time.

To combat one Rodian at a time: Choose your weapon. Add your weaponry# to your weapon's mid-range# +2 for your confront#. Roll the 12-dice to shoot at the first Rodian.

If your confront# is equal to or more than your roll#, add the difference to your MP total. Repeat the confront to combat the second Rodian.

If your confront# is lower than your roll#, subtract the difference from your MP total and repeat this confront, adding +2 to your confront# for your new confront#. Use this new confront# until you have defeated the first Rodian. Once you have defeated the first Rodian, repeat this confront with the old confront# to combat the second Rodian.

After you have defeated the two Rodians, add 30MP to your MP total. You may now proceed.

You step over to the fallen Rodians. Q-7N floats down to your side and examines the two bodies on the floor. "Let's hope they stay that way," says the droid.

"How can we get you out of here?" you ask the Vratix.

"Follow us!" Plurra yells. The Vratix scurries across the warehouse and leads you to what appears to be a brick wall. "This wall is a secret door. It will lead us outside."

The door opens to an alley. You step through it, followed by Q-7N and Plurra.

The Vratix's triangular head raises and appears to take a deep breath. "You have helped us gain our freedom," it says. "We are in your debt."

"No problem," you reply. "But before you leave, maybe you should wait here for a few minutes with Q-7N. I need to go back to that cantina and speak to the owner."

"Is that a good idea?" asks Q-7N.

"No," you respond. "But I'm feeling a lot less friendly this time around."

You leave the alley and step onto the main street. After crossing over to the cantina, you step through the entrance.

The goggled Kubaz is still sitting at the counter. The Devaronian is polishing glasses behind the counter. Neither one of them is looking in your direction. The stool and trapdoor are back in place. Everything seems normal.

But the other creatures in the cantina notice you and see the menace in your gaze. Chairs scrape against the floor and customers walk, slither, and crawl out the door. The Devaronian looks up at you. His eyes go wide with surprise.

"What you did to me was wrong," you say through clenched teeth. "But what you did to that Vratix was even worse!" Hearing your voice, the Kubaz whirls around with his blaster drawn.

You must combat the Kubaz.

To combat the Kubaz: Choose your weapon. Add your weaponry# to your weapon's close-range# for your confront#. Roll the 6-dice to neutralize the Kubaz.

> *If your confront# is equal to or more than your roll#,* add the difference to your MP total. The Kubaz is no longer a threat to anyone.

> *If your confront# is less than your roll#,* subtract the difference from your MP total and repeat this confront until you have neutralized the Kubaz.

The Devaronian watches as the Kubaz falls to the floor. "How did you escape?" the Devaronian asks.

"Ask your henchmen!" you snarl. "Now tell me how to get to Morbo's Place."

Trembling with fear, the Devaronian gives you detailed instructions.

"One more thing," you demand. "What's the name of your cantina?"

"The Plastoid Pitt," replies the confused Devaronian.

"Thanks," you reply. "I'll remember that." You leave the cantina and return to the alley.

"I've got new directions to Morbo's Place," you announce.

"Do we go there now?" Q-7N asks.

"First we're going back to rescue the other Rebels. They must be in the cell blocks."

"We will help you," declares the Vratix.

"Thanks, Plurra," you reply. "We can make it back to

Docking Bay Seventy-two on foot. We'll pick up the Y-wing later."

Q-7N soars through the alleys of Zalxuc City, guiding you and Plurra back to the docking bay. You peek around the corner of a building to see that the stormtroopers still have the *Falcon* surrounded.

"Imperials usually set up a base," you say. "There's probably a temporary headquarters around here."

Q-7N rotates all three photoreceptors at you and asks, "What about that office we entered earlier? The one with the two Imperial technicians?"

"Of course!" you exclaim. "Why didn't I think of that before? There was a comm unit in my cell. If we make it to that office, I should be able to contact the other Rebels!"

You keep your head down as you make your way back to the basement-level office. The stormtroopers will remember your face from when you were brought in, and you don't have an available disguise. You enter an alleyway.

When you are nearly at the door that leads to the office, you see three stormtroopers guarding the door.

"If I'm going to get rid of those guys," you contemplate, "I'll have to draw them into this alley." You turn to Plurra and whisper your instructions.

Turning to Q-7N, you instruct the droid to rise up into the sky over the *Millennium Falcon*. When the droid questions you, you tell it that you will explain later.

Q-7N rises up into the sky. You back into the alley as Plurra races out to stand before the three stormtroopers.

"Help!" yells Plurra to the stormtroopers. "There's an escaped Rebel!"

"Show us where!" commands one of the troopers.

With the stormtroopers following, Plurra races back into the alley where you are waiting. When Plurra is thirty meters away from you, the Vratix jumps up to the roof in a single leap. The startled stormtroopers are now lined up one after the other in the alley.

You must combat all three stormtroopers.

To combat the stormtroopers: Choose your weapon. Add your weaponry# to your weapon's mid-range# +3 for your confront#. Roll the 12-dice to combat the first stormtrooper.

> *If your confront# is equal to or more than your roll#,* add the difference to your MP total. You may proceed to combat the second stormtrooper, using the same confront equation.

> *If your confront# is lower than your roll#,* subtract the difference from your MP total. Now add +4 to your confront# for your new confront#. Roll the 12-dice again to continue to combat the first stormtrooper.

> > *If your new confront# is equal to or more than your roll#,* add the difference to your MP total. You may proceed to combat the second stormtrooper, using the same confront equation. Repeat this confront equation until you have defeated the third stormtrooper.

> > *If your new confront# is less than your roll#,* subtract the difference from your MP total. Repeat this con-

front with your new confront# until you have defeated all three stormtroopers.

Once you have defeated all three stormtroopers, you may
proceed. That wasn't easy. Add 25MP to your MP total (40MP
for Advanced Level players).

You race into the office, but there's no sign of the technicians. You look over the comm switchboard and log onto
the local Imperial frequency. "Attention all stormtroopers!"
you announce into the comm. "There is a Rebel uprising at
a cantina called the Plastoid Pitt! All troopers are to report
to the Plastoid Pitt immediately!"

"What about the prisoners, sir?" asks a stormtrooper
over the comm.

"I said *all* stormtroopers, soldier!" you bark into
comm. "Now move!"

One minute later, you push a series of buttons linked
to a chain of cell blocks. Switching the comm to a different frequency, you speak into the comm. "Okay, everyone,"
you address your imprisoned friends. "I'm in an Imperial
control room. I've gotten rid of the stormtroopers and just
opened all of your cell doors. When you step outside, look
up to the sky to locate Q-7N. He's hovering directly over the
Falcon. I'll meet you there in five minutes!"

"Thanks," calls a voice over the comm.

"What took you so long?" grouses another.

You raise your weapon and fire a blast into the computer console. That should buy you some more time.

You run out of the office and nearly smash into a single
stormtrooper.

"All the other troopers have gone to the Plastoid Pitt," snarls the trooper. "But I thought I recognized your voice. Only now you're in the flesh." The trooper raises his weapon.

You can choose to dodge the stormtrooper or combat him. You must choose now.

To dodge the stormtrooper (without Power): Add your skill# to your strength# +3 for your confront#. Roll the 12-dice to dodge the stormtrooper.

> *If your confront# is equal to or more than your roll#*, add the difference to your MP total. You have successfully dodged the stormtrooper and tricked him into accidentally shooting himself. You may proceed.

> *If your confront# is lower than your roll#*, subtract the difference from your MP total. You cannot avoid the trooper. You must fight him (below).

To dodge the stormtrooper (using Power)*: Choose your Evasion Power. Add your skill# to your Jedi# to your Power's mid-resist# for your confront#. Roll the 6-dice to dodge the stormtrooper.

> *If your confront# is equal to or more than your roll#*, add the difference to your MP total and proceed.

> *If your confront# is lower than your roll#*, subtract the difference from your MP total. You cannot dodge the trooper. You must fight him (below).

*Note: This counts as one of two Power uses you are allowed in this Mission.

To combat the stormtrooper: Choose your weapon. Add your weaponry# to your weapon's mid-range# +3 for your confront#. Roll the 12-dice to shoot the stormtrooper.

If your confront# is equal to or more than your roll#, add the difference to your MP total. You may proceed.

If your confront# is lower than your roll#, subtract the difference from your MP total and repeat this confront, adding +2 to your confront# for your new confront#. Once you have defeated the stormtrooper, you may proceed.

That was one very difficult stormtrooper. Add 40MP to your MP total (45MP for Advanced Level players).

Plurra leaps down from the roof and rushes to your side. "We thank you for your help," says the Vratix. "If you don't mind, we wish to return to our family now."

"The Rebellion thanks *you*, Plurra," you say with a smile. "Take care of yourself." The Vratix leaps away.

You return to Docking Bay 72 to find your friends already on board the *Falcon*.

"Hurry up!" a voice calls from the ship. "The Imperials might be back any minute! We've got to hide the *Falcon* in a different hangar!"

"I'm coming!" you reply as you race to the ship. Q-7N swoops down from the sky, returning to your side.

"Are we leaving Thyferra?" asks the floating droid.

"Not yet," you reply. "We've got to pick up the Y-wing. And then we're going to Morbo's Place!"

For saving the Rebels and escaping from the stormtroopers, add 200MP to your MP total.

THE
AFTER-
MISSION

The Rebels and the droids entered the cantina.

The inside of Morbo's Place was fairly clean, and the customers — a mixed crowd of aliens and humans — appeared friendly. It didn't look like the kind of place that would encourage fighting. Threepio and Artoo were surprised to see a small group of chattering droids seated in one corner.

Artoo emitted a series of whooping beeps.

"I agree with you entirely, Artoo!" Threepio stated. "Morbo's Place seems most civilized!"

Solo went directly to a huge blue alien who stood behind a counter. "Is Voralla in?" he asked.

"Morbo?" the alien called to the room behind the counter. "Some people are here to see you."

Voralla Morbo stepped out from the back room and entered the cantina. She was a tall, striking woman, and wore dark green coveralls with high brown boots. The color of her short hair reminded Luke of the deserts on Tatooine.

Morbo scanned the small band of Rebels. Her eyes drifted from Chewbacca to remain fixed on Han Solo. "Well, well, well," she said, "if it isn't Chewbacca the Wookiee and his pet human."

"Hi, Voralla," Solo said. "It's been a long time."

"Yeah, it has," Morbo agreed. "But I haven't forgotten that I owe you this." Morbo launched her left arm through the air and caught Solo under the chin. Solo fell backward onto the floor with a loud thud. Luke bent down to help his friend get up.

"This seems to be your day for getting hit," Leia said to Han. "Why didn't you tell us that you knew Voralla Morbo?"

"Well, nobody *asked* me," Solo replied. Chewbacca rolled his eyes and looked at the ceiling. Solo often found himself in squabbles like this and it brought great amusement to the Wookiee.

Standing, Solo turned to Morbo. "Look, Morbo, I can understand if you're still upset because I couldn't deliver the shipment of Norvanian grog to you. The distributor on Ban-Satir II had a little trouble, and I had to take on another job. For what it's worth, I'm very, very sorry."

Morbo shook her head. "I'm not upset about the Norvanian grog, Solo." She took a step closer to Solo and the captain of the *Millennium Falcon* took two steps backward. Then Morbo smiled and added, "I'm just angry because you never asked me out on a date."

Solo exhaled. "Oh," he said. "That."

Chewbacca could no longer contain himself. Loud Wookiee laughter burst from his mouth.

"This is all very entertaining," Leia interrupted as she turned to Morbo, "but we have a very important matter to discuss. Is there somewhere we can talk?"

Morbo led the Rebels into the back room. The droids followed.

"I'll bet I know why you've come to Thyferra," opined Morbo. "It's about bacta, isn't it?"

"How did you know *that*?" asked Luke.

Morbo turned to Luke and addressed him as if he were a child. "Sweetie, why does *anyone* come to Thyferra?"

Luke blushed. He'd never been called "sweetie" before.

"You've helped the Rebellion in the past, Morbo," Leia said, trying to maintain order. "We need information. Do you know if the Empire recently obtained an unusually large amount of bacta?"

"The *Empire*?" laughed Morbo. "No, the Empire likes to make money off bacta, but they're not exactly in the healing business. Sorry I can't help."

Leia sighed. "Well, if you do hear of anything odd," she said, "please let us know."

"Odd, huh?" Morbo wondered. "Now that you mention it, I did hear something rather strange."

"Please, Morbo," Solo requested. "Just tell us."

Morbo grinned. "For you, Solo, anything. I heard that there was an Imperial ship on Thyferra a few weeks ago, and that they picked up an enormous supply of alazhi."

"Alazhi?" Q-7N exclaimed. "A Vratix told us that alazhi is used to make bacta."

"That's right," confirmed Morbo. "Alazhi only grows on Thyferra. No other planet has been able to grow alazhi. That's why I thought the Imperial pickup was odd. What would the Empire do with so much alazhi?"

"Maybe they're trying to grow it on another planet," suggested Solo.

"Morbo, do you have any idea where the Imperial ship was headed?" asked Leia.

"I've got my sources," replied Morbo. "A friend of mine overheard a stormtrooper mention something about the Delrakkin system."

"Delrakkin?" said Solo with surprise. "That's quite a haul, almost beyond the Outer Rim! What kind of model was this Imperial ship that came to Thyferra?"

"That's what I really remember," replied Morbo. "I'd

never seen a ship quite like it. It was a modified Carrack cruiser. It only carried three TIE fighters."

A stunned silence fell across the Rebels. Luke turned to Han and Leia and said, "It's probably the same ship that crashed on Yavin Four!"

"It's got to be," agreed Solo. "That ship is one of a kind."

"Could the Empire be trying to grow bacta on Delrakkin?" Leia wondered aloud. "Or do the Imperials intend to poison the people of Delrakkin with contaminated bacta?"

"There's only one way to tell for certain," Solo said as he turned to Chewbacca. The Wookiee nodded in agreement.

"Then what are we standing here for?" Luke rallied. "We've got to go to Delrakkin!"

NEXT: ATTACK ON DELRAKKIN!